VIR! FIX ME A DRINK!

—FOR YOU, MR. MORDEN?

NO, THANK YOU. THERE IS *ONE* MORE THING.

SHOULD MR. GARIBALDI DECIDE TO INVESTIGATE THIS MATTER FURTHER, WE WOULD APPRECIATE YOUR TELLING US.

GOOD DAY, AMBASSADOR.

WITH YOU, THERE ALWAYS IS.

MAYBE I SHOULD JUST THROW MR. GARIBALDI OUT THE NEAREST AIRLOCK *NOW*.

AMBASSADOR! MR. GARIBALDI IS YOUR *FRIEND*. YOU *WOULDN'T* DISCUSS HIS BUSINESS WITH THIS MORDEN... *WOULD* YOU? YOU KNOW NOTHING ABOUT MORDEN!

ENOUGH, VIR. MY LIFE IS GETTING TOO COMPLICATED. IT IS *TIME* TO CALL IN *REINFORCEMENTS*.

"ANYTHING ON GOLD CHANNEL?"

"NADA."

WHAT EXACTLY ARE WE *LOOKING* FOR?

GREMLINS. BIG BALD PEACOCK GREMLINS WITH BIG FLAPPING MOUTHS.

IMPENDING DEMOTION AT FOUR O'CLOCK.

AH, MR. GARIBALDI. MY *APOLOGIES*. WHEN I ASKED TO SEE YOU IN C&C ABOUT THE DRAZI TRANSPORT MANIFEST AN HOUR AGO, I DIDN'T REALIZE *I* WAS SUPPOSED TO INTERRUPT MY BUSY SCHEDULE AND COME DOWN *HERE* TO *YOU*.

MMM...

SHALL I START COMPOSING YOUR EULOGY NOW, OR WOULD YOU LIKE TO EXPLAIN YOURSELF.

I PERFORM RANDOM CHECKS ON DIPLOMATIC TRANSMISSIONS, LOOKING FOR UNAUTHORIZED OR ILLEGAL ACTIVITIES. TWO DAYS AGO, I PICKED UP AN ODD INCOMING MESSAGE.

THIS PARTICULAR MESSAGE CONTAINED EMBEDDED INFORMATION ABOUT NARN FLEET BUILD-UPS IN AN OUTLYING SECTOR OF THE CENTAURI EMPIRE.

THERE'S NOTHING OUT-OF-THE-ORDINARY ABOUT THAT.

THERE'S MORE. A LITTLE WHILE AGO, G'KAR AS GOOD AS ACCUSED LONDO OF BETRAYING A NARN SHIP INTO BEING DESTROYED ON THE RIM.

HEARSAY, MR. GARIBALDI.

GOTCHA!

WHAT IS IT?

HE'S A CLEVER ONE, THIS GREMLIN. IF I TAP INTO HIS SIGNAL THE WRONG WAY, HE'LL KNOW AND SHUT DOWN...

I HAVE NO CHOICE—THE ONLY WAY I CAN EAVESDROP IS TO PIGGYBACK ON THE *INCOMING* TRANSMISSION... I WON'T BE ABLE TO SEE WHO'S SENDING. I'LL ONLY SEE WHO'S RECEIVING.

AND HOW IS THE EMPEROR'S HEALTH?

ALL RIGHT, MR. GARIBALDI. LET'S SEE YOUR GREMLIN.

NOT GOOD. IT WON'T BE LONG NOW. SOON WE MUST BE READY TO MOVE. ARE YOU READY?

I'M NOT SURE.

YOUR SOURCE TOOK CARE OF A NARN MILITARY OUTPOST VERY IMPRESSIVELY. WHAT WORRIES YOU NOW?

LET ME TALK TO SHERIDAN.

HE'S NOT GONNA BELIEVE ME. YOU *KNOW* ME. YOU *KNOW* MY HUNCHES PAN OUT. COMMANDER *SINCLAIR* KNEW IT. SINCLAIR WOULD OKAY THIS!

CHIEF, AMBASSADOR MOLLARI HAS JUST ARRANGED TRANSPORT ON A CENTAURI PERSONAL TRANSPORT. DEPARTURE IN ONE HOUR.

PLEASE, COMMANDER...

I'LL SPEAK TO THE CAPTAIN.

STAY *RIGHT* HERE.

ONE...

...TWO...

...THREE.

AND WE'RE OFF.

DON'T TRY TO STOP ME, WARREN. THIS IS IMPORTANT. AND DANGEROUS.

WITH ME? THEN SHERIDAN OKAYED THE MISSION?

STOP YOU? I'M GOING WITH YOU.

I HAVE NO IDEA WHAT YOU'RE TALKING ABOUT, CHIEF. I JUST KNOW THAT I DRIVE THIS THING BETTER THAN YOU. SO IF YOU'RE OFF TO DO SOMETHING DANGEROUS...

...IT'S MY DUTY TO GO, TOO.

AND I CAN'T LET YOU GO ALONE, CHIEF. SOMEBODY HAS TO BRING YOU BACK ALIVE.

I CAN'T ASK YOU TO SHARE THE RISK, KEFFER.

LET'S GO, THEN.

I KNEW YOU'D SEE IT MY WAY.

LONDO'S QUARTERS

AMBASSADOR, I THINK IT'S A MISTAKE FOR YOU TO LEAVE THE STATION.

THAT IS WHY *I* AM THE AMBASSADOR AND *YOU* ARE THE AIDE, VIR.

STOP *THINKING* SO MUCH AND START *HELPING*.

I'LL BE BACK SOON, VIR.

GREAT MAKER, PROTECT HIM.

HMF. NEVER A LIFT WHEN YOU NEED ONE...

AHA! IT'S ABOUT TIME—

ACK!

HELLO, AMBASSADOR. PLEASE, JOIN ME.

IT'S ALL RIGHT, AMBASSADOR. YOU'VE DONE US A FAVOR.

COME IN AND WE'LL TALK.

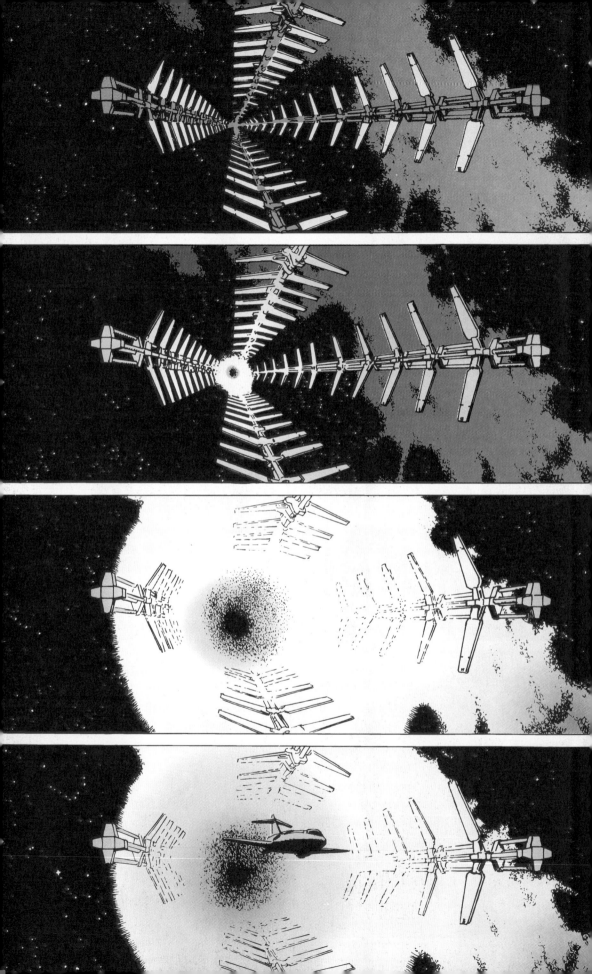

MARS COLONY.

"I'D BEEN FIRED FROM MY LAST COUPLE OF GIGS. I STARTED A *SHUTTLE TRANSPORT SERVICE* TO THE OUTLYING REGIONS. MOSTLY PEOPLE WHO DIDN'T LIKE BEING ASKED QUESTIONS ABOUT THEIR BUSINESS.

"FINE WITH ME. ASKING QUESTIONS ALWAYS SEEMED TO GET ME INTO *TROUBLE.*

"I WAS LOOKING FOR COMFORT IN A BOTTLE WHEN MY LIFE CHANGED—*PERMANENTLY.*"

MR. GARIBALDI...

LIEUTENANT COMMANDER SINCLAIR, EARTHFORCE. I NEED TO HIRE OUT YOUR SERVICES AS A SHUTTLE PILOT.

YEAH? MUST BE A DOOZY OF A MISSION FOR YOU TO COME *HERE.*

WHY IS THAT?

MOST OF THE PEOPLE WHO HIRE ME DON'T WANT ANY QUESTIONS ASKED AND I OBLIGE THEM.

I NEED SOMEONE FAMILIAR WITH THIS PART OF MARS. I HEARD YOU WERE THE BEST. MAYBE I HEARD WRONG.

YOU HEARD RIGHT, LIEUTENANT COMMANDER.

I KNOW THIS AREA LIKE THE BACK OF MY HAND.

MORE LIKE THE BOTTOM OF A BOTTLE.

I PREFER MY PILOTS SOBER.

AND I LIKE MY CLIENTS TO RESPECT MY PRIVACY, JUST LIKE I RESPECT THEIRS.

DON'T WORRY, COMMANDER BIGSHOT. I'LL GET YOU WHERE YOU NEED TO GO.

MY RESPONSIBILITY IS TO MY PEOPLE. I WON'T HAVE YOU ENDANGERING THEIR LIVES.

WHATEVER. WE LEAVE IN ONE HOUR.

BE READY.

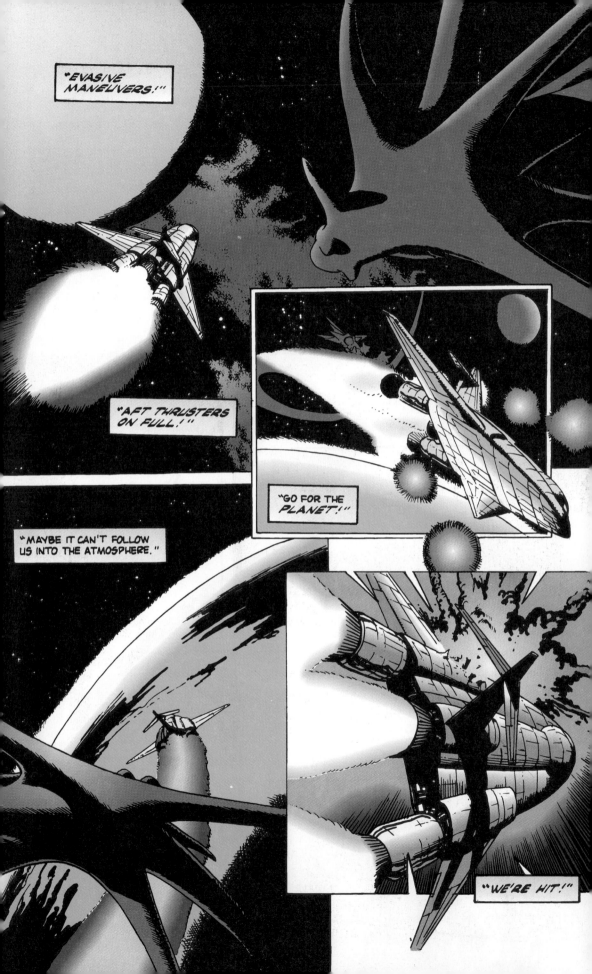

TO BE CONTINUED...

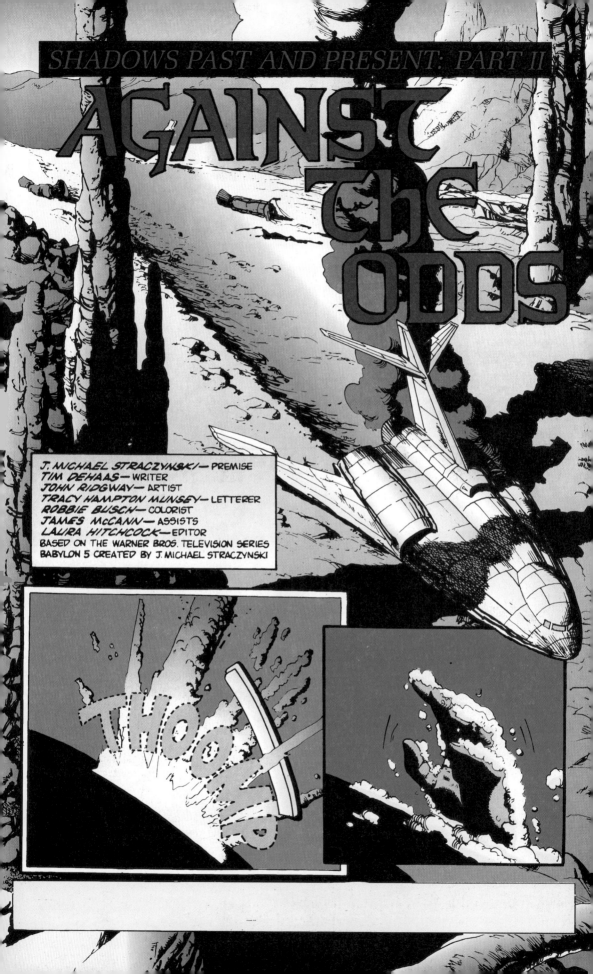

"YEAH. REMEMBER I WAS TELLING YOU HOW I FIRST MET COMMANDER SINCLAIR, BACK ON MARS, YEARS AGO?"

HOW CAN WE DO RECONNAISSANCE MISSIONS WHEN WE DON'T EVEN KNOW WHAT WE'RE LOOKING FOR? SOUNDS LIKE TWO WEEKS OF BUSY WORK, TO ME. AND WHY USE A *CIVILIAN* TRANSPORT?

EARTHFORCE *ALWAYS* HAS A REASON, FOSTER.

SHOWS HOW MUCH *YOU* KNOW, SANCHEZ. WHEN YOU'VE BEEN AROUND AS LONG AS *I* HAVE—

LISTEN TO YOU! GUY GETS HIS COMMISSION *SIX MONTHS* AHEAD OF ME—

—NOW HE THINKS HE'S A FREAKIN' *COLONEL!*

OH, YEAH—?

ANY SIGN OF OUR *PILOT?*

NO, *LIEUTENANT COMMANDER SINCLAIR.* WE'VE BEEN HERE ABOUT TWENTY MINUTES. NO SIGN OF *GARIBALDI!*

I EXPECTED AS MUCH.

SHOULD WE ORGANIZE A SEARCH TEAM?

GIVEN WHAT WE'VE SEEN OF HIM SO FAR, I'D SUGGEST STARTING AT THE LOCAL *DRINKING HOLES.*

NO... WAIT HERE.

"YEAH, WE WERE ONE BIG HAPPY FAMILY. FOSTER AND SANCHEZ WERE OKAY, THOUGH. THEY WERE YOUNG, FOLLOWING ORDERS—THEY HADN'T SEEN WHAT I'D SEEN.

"THEY DIDN'T KNOW HOW MUCH I NEEDED THE BOOZE, DIDN'T KNOW HOW I CAUSED A FRIEND'S DEATH.

"I COULDN'T FIGURE OUT SINCLAIR, THOUGH.

"RUMOR HAD IT *HE* WAS THE REASON THE MINBARI *SURRENDERED* TO US—JUST WHEN THEY WERE ON THE VERGE OF *WIPING OUT HUMANITY.*

"I'D EXPECTED SOME KIND OF CHARISMATIC *HERO TYPE.* I'VE SEEN *DEAD BODIES* THAT WEREN'T AS STIFF AS THIS GUY."

"EVERY DAY WAS THE *SAME*: GET UP, LOAD THE SHUTTLE, FILE A FLIGHT PLAN. THEN, AFTER WE'D CRUISED FOR AN HOUR, SINCLAIR WOULD GIVE ME A NEW HEADING, AND WE'D HEAD OFF IN *ANOTHER* DIRECTION."

COULD YOU BE A *LITTLE* MORE SPECIFIC?

"AFTER A FEW DAYS, I STARTED GETTING CURIOUS. ASKED SINCLAIR WHAT WE WERE LOOKING FOR. THE ONLY THING HE'D SAY WAS, 'ANYTHING THAT SHOULDN'T BE THERE.'"

OH. THANKS, THAT HELPS A *LOT*. I'LL KEEP THAT IN MIND.

JERK.

"I FIXED EVERYONE UP BEST I COULD. WE NEEDED HELP *REAL BAD*, BUT THE RADIO WAS KNOCKED OUT IN THE CRASH. NO ONE KNEW WHERE TO LOOK FOR US BECAUSE SINCLAIR HAD ME FILE A FALSE FLIGHT PLAN.

"NOT TO MENTION THE *MINIMAL ATMOSPHERE* AND *SUB-FREEZING TEMPERATURES* OUTSIDE.

"IT DIDN'T LOOK GOOD."

WELL, WE CAN *WAIT* HERE AND HOPE SOMEONE SEES US, OR WE CAN GO FOR *HELP*.

HOW FAR IS THAT?

I'D SAY ABOUT FIFTY MILES.

WHAT ABOUT *SUPPLIES*?

WE HAVE ENOUGH FOOD AND AIR FOR THREE PEOPLE FOR FIVE DAYS. I HAVE THREE ENVIRONMENT SUITS WITH 10-DAY POWER PACKS.

THREE SUITS IN A *FOUR-PERSON* SHUTTLE. AND ONLY THREE OF US LEFT. *NICE*, THE WAY THOSE NUMBERS WORKED OUT.

"SINCLAIR DECIDED HE AND I SHOULD GO FOR HELP. WE GAVE SANCHEZ ONE ENVIRONMENT SUIT AND FIVE DAYS OF AIR, TO USE IN CASE THE SHUTTLE'S SYSTEMS FAILED.

"WE PACKED EVERYTHING WE NEEDED TO SURVIVE...

"...NOT THAT I BELIEVED WE WOULD."

"I STASHED FOSTER OUTSIDE THE SHUTTLE. HE'D BE FROZEN STIFF IN LESS THAN HALF AN HOUR. BETTER THAT SANCHEZ NOT HAVE HIM FOR COMPANY."

SECURE THE PERIMETER, LIEUTENANT. NO ONE GETS IN HERE WITHOUT *IDENTIFYING* HIM OR HERSELF.

AYE, SIR. YOU CAN COUNT ON ME. AND, SIR?

YES?

KEEP AN EYE ON GARIBALDI, SIR. I DON'T THINK HE'S BAD PEOPLE, BUT I WOULDN'T PUT MY LIFE IN *HIS* HANDS IF *I* COULD HELP IT.

UNDERSTOOD, LIEUTENANT. WE'LL KEEP THE COM-LINK OPEN UNTIL WE'RE OUT OF SIGNAL RANGE.

WE'RE ALL GOING TO DIE, SINCLAIR. LET'S GET IT OVER WITH.

DON'T BE LONG, SIR.

SURVIVAL THE HARD WAY

SHADOWS PAST AND PRESENT: PART III

J. MICHAEL **STRACZYNSKI** STORY PREMISE

TIM **DeHAAS** WRITER

JOHN **RIDGWAY** ARTIST

TRACY HAMPTON **MUNSEY** LETTERER

ROBBIE **BUSCH** COLORIST

JAMES **McCANN** ASSISTS

LAURA **HITCHCOCK** EDITOR

BASED ON THE WARNER BROS. TELEVISION SERIES *BABYLON 5* CREATED BY J. MICHAEL STRACZYNSKI

SO, KEFFER, ANY SECOND THOUGHTS ABOUT BEING ON AN *UNAUTHORIZED MISSION* WITH A SOON-TO-BE *EX-HEAD OF SECURITY*?

I JUST WANT TO KNOW *ONE* THING, GARIBALDI...

NOBODY KNEW I FLEW YOU TO *THIS* SECTOR OF SPACE, YET SOME *UNKNOWN SHIP* COMES OUT OF *NOWHERE* AND *SHOOTS* US DOWN.

WHAT'S THE *SECRET* OF YOUR *POPULARITY*?

SIMPLE. CHARM AND A GREAT *PERSONALITY*.

YEAH? LET'S SEE YOU TRY YOUR CHARM ON THE GUYS THAT ARE *FOLLOWING* US.

IF THEY CAN CATCH UP.

"RIGHT. SINCLAIR AND I TOOK SHELTER IN A CAVE AND HAD TO WAIT THE STORM OUT BEFORE GOING FOR HELP.

"WITH OUR SHUTTLE *CRASHED* IN THE MIDDLE OF *NOWHERE* ON MARS...

"...AND CONSIDERING WE ONLY HAD *FIVE DAYS* OF *AIR* AND *FOOD* FOR EACH OF US, IT WASN'T EASY TO JUST *WAIT.*

"WE MAINTAINED RADIO CONTACT WITH LT. SANCHEZ, WHO'D STAYED BEHIND IN THE SHUTTLE."

RADIO CONTACT. HAH.

WHO DOES *SINCLAIR* THINK HE'S *KIDDING?* WE'RE SO FAR OUT IN THE MIDDLE OF *NOWHERE,* WE'LL BE *DEAD* BEFORE WE CAN REACH HELP.

FRANK'S *DEAD....?* NO...

MY FAULT...I SHOULD'VE BEEN THERE...

SHOULD'VE SEEN IT *COMING.*

I SHOULD HAVE *SAVED* HIM...

I'M COMING TO *GET* YOU, FRANK...

BEEP
BEEP
BEEP
BEEP
BEEP
BEEP

BEEP
BEEP
BEEP
BEEP
BEEP
BEEP

HUUUHHHH

BEEP BEEP BEEP BEEP BEEP

OH. AIR'S LOW. GOT TO REPLACE THE *CYLINDERS*.

THERE. *THAT* OUGHT TO TAKE CARE OF IT.

BEEP BEEP BEEP

STILL BEEPING? WHAT THE— OH, *CRUD*, I SHUT OFF TH' *COM*.

GARIBALDI HERE—

GARIBALDI! WHERE HAVE YOU BEEN?

HEY, NOT SO *LOUD!* I CAN HEAR YOU JUST *FINE*, SANCHEZ.

CLICK

YOU *IDIOT!* LIEUTENANT COMMANDER SINCLAIR WENT *LOOKING* FOR YOU AFTER YOU WANDERED OFF.

THERE WAS A *ROCKSLIDE* AND HE CAN'T GET BACK INTO THE CAVE! HE'S OUT OF AIR AND *SUFFOCATING*.

I CAN'T *RAISE* HIM. I THINK HE *BLACKED OUT!*

OH, MY GOD...

HOW LONG AGO?

FIVE MINUTES.

WHAT THE—

WHAT THE *HELL* WERE YOU *DOING?*

DO SOMETHING *STUPID* LIKE THAT *AGAIN*, AND I'LL MAKE SURE YOU *GET* YOUR *DEATH WISH.*

YOU WANT MY SCALP, *SINCLAIR?* COME AND *GET* IT.

WELL, WELL, SO YOU'VE GOT SOME *FIGHT* IN YOU AFTER ALL.

I CAN FEEL MY CHANCES FOR SURVIVAL *IMPROVING* ALREADY.

BUT IF SINCLAIR HAD BEEN *INSIDE* THE CAVE WHEN IT COLLAPSED, HE WOULD HAVE HAD *ZERO* CHANCE OF SURVIVAL.

YEAH. I SAVED HIS LIFE *TWICE.*

J. MICHAEL STRACZYNSKI—STORY PREMISE
TIM DeHAAS—WRITER
JOHN RIDGWAY—ARTIST
TRACY HAMPTON MUNSEY—LETTERER
ROBBIE BUSCH—COLORIST
JAMES McCANN—ASSISTS
LAURA HITCHCOCK—EDITOR
BASED ON THE WARNER BROS. TELEVISION
SERIES BABYLON 5 CREATED BY
J. MICHAEL STRACZYNSKI.

"I WONDERED, WAS *THIS* THE *MYSTERY THING* SINCLAIR HAD BEEN LOOKING FOR?

"BUT HE LOOKED AS SURPRISED AS I WAS.

"AND PROBABLY DIDN'T WANT ANYONE TO KNOW IT *WAS*.

"WE HAD TWO CYLINDERS APIECE LEFT. THAT MEANT WE HAD ONLY *THREE HOURS* TO FIND ANOTHER SUPPLY OF AIR BEFORE *WE SUFFOCATED.*"

"I'D NEVER SEEN SHIPS LIKE THAT BEFORE. I HAD NO IDEA WHO THEY BELONGED TO..."

"AND NO IDEA IF SINCLAIR KNEW..."

"...BUT I WAS ABOUT TO FIND OUT."

"THE ENEMY I FEAR MOST IS THE ENEMY I DON'T KNOW.

"HE OR SHE—OR IT—CAN GET YOU *ANYWHERE*, ANY *TIME*.

"*NO* RULES. *NO* MERCY."

"SINCLAIR DIDN'T RUSH UP TO GREET THE NEW ARRIVALS, SO I ASSUMED HE DIDN'T RECOGNIZE THEM, EITHER.

"UP UNTIL NOW, I DIDN'T KNOW ALL THAT MUCH ABOUT SINCLAIR.

"THAT WAS CHANGING, THOUGH."

"I'VE ALWAYS GONE WITH MY *GUT INSTINCT.* KIND OF A SURVIVAL THING.

"OUR COMS WERE BEING JAMMED, WHICH, TO MY KNOWLEDGE, MEANT *ALL* COMMUNICATIONS WERE JAMMED.

"THAT MEANT THE OTHER GUYS HAD TO USE AN *ALTERNATIVE* WAY TO COMMUNICATE..."

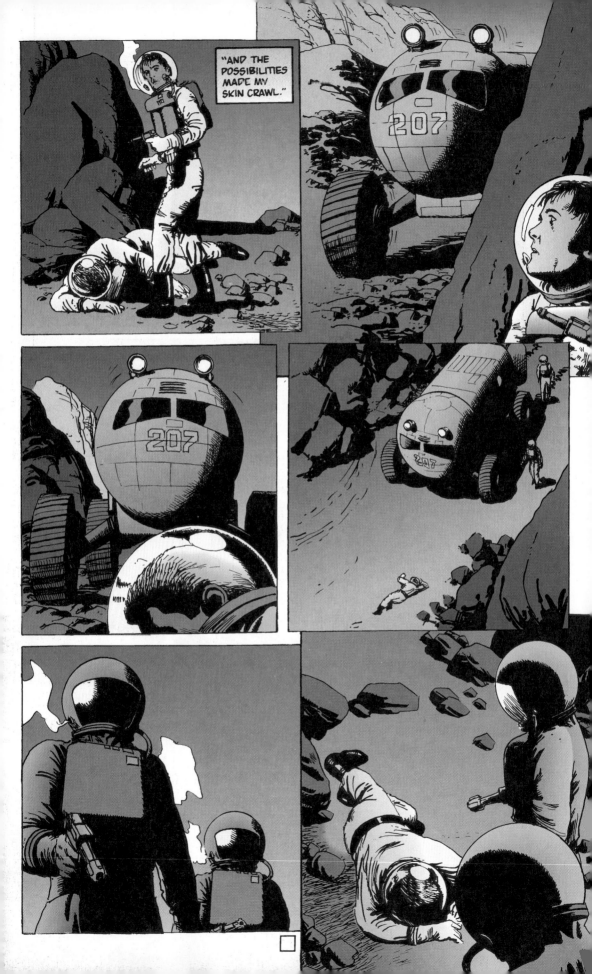

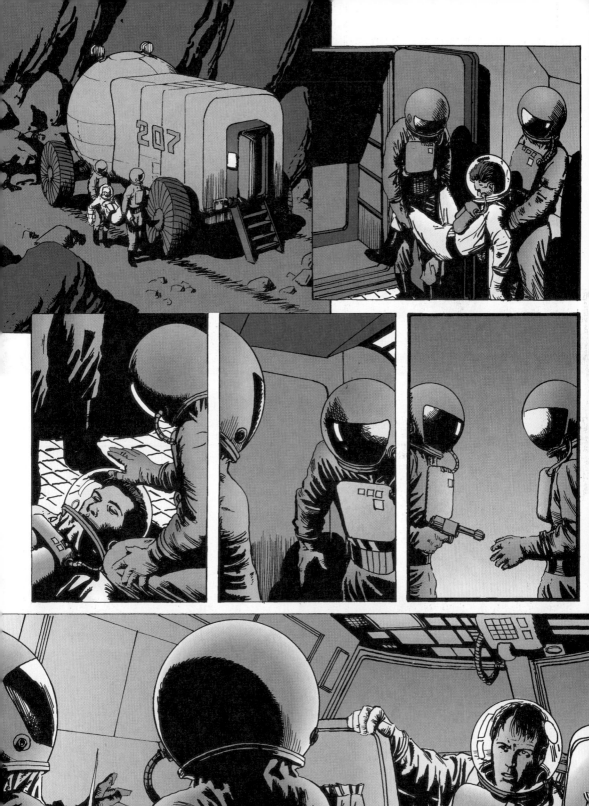

"WE'D PASSED THE POINT OF NO RETURN. THE ONLY OPTION WAS TO TRY TO *BLEND IN* WITH THE REST OF THEM."

"THERE WAS NO SOUND, EXCEPT FOR MY OWN BREATHING. I JUST READ THEIR BODY LANGUAGE AS BEST I COULD AND PLAYED ALONG.

"SINCLAIR STAYED INSIDE THE CRAWLER WHILE I GOT OUT. I DIDN'T WANT THEM SEEING HIS BROKEN WRIST.

"SOONER OR LATER, THOUGH, WE'D BE FOUND OUT.

"BUT IT SURE FELT GOOD TO HAVE THAT RUSH OF *ADRENALINE* GOING THROUGH MY SYSTEM AGAIN."

"THE PENALTY FOR SPYING IS EXECUTION, MR. KEFFER AND MR. GARIBALDI."

LOOK, JUST CALL THE STATION—CALL BABYLON 5 AND SPEAK TO CAPTAIN SHERIDAN. HE'LL CORROBORATE OUR STORY.

YEAH, *RIGHT,* KEFFER. THEN HE CAN EXECUTE US *HIMSELF* FOR GOING ON AN UNAUTHORIZED MISSION.

WE'VE JUST COMPLETED AN INVESTIGATION OF YOUR CLAIMS. THERE IS *NO EVIDENCE* THAT A SHIP CRASHED AT THE SITE YOU DESCRIBED.

QUIET!

BUT I— OOF!

NEITHER DID WE SEE SIGNS OF A FIGHT IN THE CLEARING YOU MENTIONED. AND YOU STILL HAVEN'T EXPLAINED *WHY* YOU WERE *NEAR* THIS PLANET IN THE *FIRST* PLACE.

HMM, BABYLON 5... AMBASSADOR LONDO MOLLARI IS STATIONED THERE, IS HE NOT?

AMBASSADOR MOLLARI! THE GREAT MAN WHO RECOVERED QUADRANT 37 FOR US FROM THE NARN!

UH, HE *MIGHT* BE THERE...

QUADRANT 37?! SO LONDO *IS* INVOLVED! I *KNEW* IT!

I WILL CONTACT AMBASSADOR MOLLARI AND CONFIRM YOUR STORY WITH HIM.

THAT'S IT. WE'RE DEAD.

IF HE CONFIRMS IT, I WILL RELEASE YOU TO HIS CUSTODY.

IF NOT, YOU WILL BE EXECUTED.

YES, MAYOR LINDAK, I GAVE MY FRIEND MR. GARIBALDI AND HIS ASSOCIATE PERMISSION TO PASS THROUGH THAT SECTOR OF SPACE.

PLEASE FORGIVE MY *INCOMPETENT* ASSISTANT FOR FORGETTING TO *NOTIFY* YOU. I *ASSURE* YOU, IT WILL *NOT* HAPPEN AGAIN.

I *APPRECIATE* THAT, AMBASSADOR. WHAT WOULD YOU LIKE ME TO *DO* WITH THEM?

I WILL TRANSFER YOU TO COMMANDER IVANOVA. SHE WILL MAKE THE NECESSARY ARRANGEMENTS.

I'M LOOKING FORWARD TO BUYING YOU A DRINK *SOON*, MR. GARIBALDI!

BREEP!

PLEASE MAKE CERTAIN I AM NOT DISTURBED AGAIN, VIR.

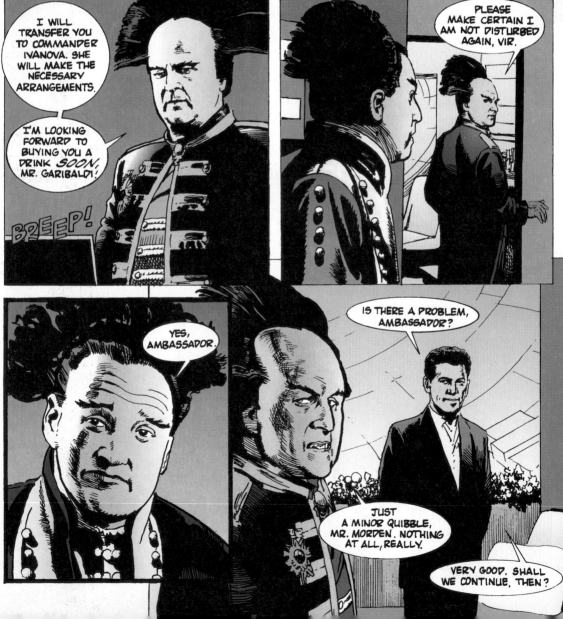

YES, AMBASSADOR.

IS THERE A PROBLEM, AMBASSADOR?

JUST A MINOR QUIBBLE, MR. MORDEN. NOTHING AT ALL, REALLY.

VERY GOOD. SHALL WE CONTINUE, THEN?

"IT SEEMS YOUR ATTEMPT TO PROVE LONDO WAS CONDUCTING *ILLEGAL BUSINESS* WAS FOR *NOTHING*, MR. GARIBALDI."

AMBASSADOR MOLLARI CONDUCTED A ROUTINE INSPECTION OF A CENTAURI COLONY AND RETURNED DIRECTLY TO BABYLON 5.

HE WAS NEVER EVEN *NEAR* THE PLANET WHERE YOU AND KEFFER CRASH-LANDED.

THEN HE MUST HAVE ANTICIPATED ME AND CHANGED HIS PLANS AT THE LAST MINUTE, CAPTAIN SHERIDAN.

IS THAT SO?

YOU TELL SOME *FANTASTIC* STORIES, MR. GARIBALDI.

I'M FAMILIAR WITH EARTHFORCE ACTIVITIES DURING THE PERIOD OF TIME YOU WERE ON MARS. AND I DON'T RECALL ANY MENTION OF THE MISSION YOU'VE DESCRIBED WITH SINCLAIR...

...AND I STILL DON'T SEE WHAT IT HAS TO DO WITH YOUR BEING SHOT DOWN OVER A CENTAURI PLANET.

SO, HOW'D IT GO?

STILL IN ONE PIECE. STILL EMPLOYED.

WHAT DO YOU THINK, GARIBALDI? IS IT POSSIBLE *ANYONE* SURVIVED THOSE EXPLOSIONS ON MARS?

I DON'T KNOW...

"HARD TO SEE HOW *ANYONE* COULD HAVE SURVIVED."

WINTERS T.

DID YOU SHOW CAPTAIN SHERIDAN WHAT YOU FOUND ON MARS?

YUP. AND ONE OF THESE DAYS, KEFFER, WE'RE GOING TO FIND OUT WHO OWNS...

...THIS *PSI-CORPS* BADGE.

THE END.